Financial Planning Workbook

TO ACCOMPANY

Personal Finance

SECOND EDITION

Jeff Madura

PEARSON

Addison
Wesley

Boston San Francisco New York
London Toronto Sydney Tokyo Singapore Madrid
Mexico City Munich Paris Cape Town Hong Kong Montreal

Contents

Preface

This Financial Planning Workbook is packaged with every new copy of *Personal Finance*, Second Edition by Jeff Madura. Notice the CD-ROM with the Financial Planning Software that is packaged in the back of the Financial Planning Workbook. Use the Financial Planning Workbook and the Financial Planning Software as a guide to completing your textbook's three main case features:

Building Your Own Financial Plan

This case feature guides you through the process of developing your own financial plan. At the end of each chapter, you complete a portion of your plan; by the end of the course you will have completed a plan that you can implement beyond the school term.

The Sampsons: A Continuing Case

This case feature prompts you to build a financial plan for a family based on information provided about their background, goals, and financial situation. The parents of two young children, Dave and Sharon Sampson have made few plans to date regarding their financial future and are eager to start saving toward a new car, their children's college education, and their retirement.

Brad Brooks: A Continuing Case

This financial planning case at the end of each part prompts you to build a financial plan for Brad Brooks based on his background and financial situation. Brad has expensive tastes—as evidenced by his soaring credit card balance—and needs assistance in gaining control of his finances.

Designed to run in Excel 97, Excel 2000, and Excel XP, the software templates aid in calculations and provide an easy way of inputting responses to the case questions. The software templates prompt you through the key steps in the financial decision-making process as you complete the *Building Your Own Financial Plan* exercises. The software's true power lies in the linking of all the worksheets; you will be directed to revise the goals, cash flow statement, and personal balance sheet to demonstrate your understanding of the interrelationships among your financial decisions. At the end of the semester, the software allows you to print out an overall financial plan consisting of the decisions you made in each chapter and the final versions of your personal goals, personal balance sheet, personal cash flow statement, and asset allocation chart. Creating a complete and integrated plan has never been this easy!

Additional software features include the following:

- New calculation-based templates on topics such as determining your federal income tax liability, reconciling a checking account, estimating the time it will take to pay off credit card debt, and determining disability insurance needs.

- For decisions that require time value of money analysis, the software directs students for input and then performs the calculations.

- Enhanced graphics such as pie charts and bar graphs that are generated based on user input aid students in visualizing their cash outflows and asset allocation.

Special acknowledgment is due to several individuals who made significant contributions to the Financial Planning Workbook and accompanying software. Steven L. Christian of Jackson Community College and Terry L. Christian of W.A. Foote Memorial Hospital developed content for the *Building Your Own Financial Plan* exercises and workbook templates. Michael P. Griffin of the University of Massachusetts, Dartmouth, developed the Excel-based Financial Planning Software.

Building Your Own Financial Plan

Chapter 1: Overview of a Financial Plan

Goals

1. Evaluate your current financial situation.
2. Set short-term, intermediate-term, and long-term goals.

Analysis

1. Complete the Personal Financial Goals template below.

Personal Financial Goals

Financial Goal	Dollar Amount to Accomplish	Priority (Low, Medium, High)
Short-Term Goals		
1.		
2.		
3.		
4.		
5.		
Intermediate-Term Goals		
1.		
2.		
3.		
4.		
5.		
Long-Term Goals		
1.		
2.		
3.		
4.		
5.		

2. A key part of the process of establishing your goals is evaluating your financial situation and career choices. Go to the "Occupational Outlook Handbook, 2002–03 Edition" (http://www.bls.gov/oco/home.htm) and research two careers that are of interest to you. Complete the template below with the information you find on this Web site.

Personal Career Goals

	Career One	Career Two
Job Title	_____	_____
Educational Requirements	_____	_____
Advancement Potential	_____	_____
Job Outlook	_____	_____
Salary Range	_____	_____
Continuing Education Requirements	_____	_____
Related Occupations	_____	_____
Brief Description of Working Conditions	_____	_____
	_____	_____
	_____	_____
	_____	_____
Brief Job Description	_____	_____
	_____	_____
	_____	_____
	_____	_____
	_____	_____

Decisions

1. Describe your strategies for reaching the goals you set.

Chapter 2: Planning with Personal Financial Statements

Goals

1. Determine how to increase net cash flows in the near future.
2. Determine how to increase net cash flows in the distant future.

Analysis

1. Prepare your personal cash flow statement.

Personal Cash Flow Statement

Cash Inflows	This Month
Disposable (after-tax) income	
Interest on deposits	
Dividend payments	
Other	
Total Cash Inflows	
Cash Outflows	
Rent/Mortgage	
Cable TV	
Electricity and water	
Telephone	
Groceries	
Health care insurance and expenses	
Clothing	
Car expenses (insurance, maintenance, and gas)	
Recreation	
Other	
Total Cash Outflows	
Net Cash Flows	

If you enter your cash flow information in the Excel template, the software will create a pie chart of your cash outflows.

2. Prepare your personal balance sheet.

Personal Balance Sheet

Assets

Liquid Assets	
Cash	
Checking account	
Savings account	
Other liquid assets	
Total liquid assets	
Household Assets	
Home	
Car	
Furniture	
Other household assets	
Total household assets	
Investment Assets	
Stocks	
Bonds	
Mutual Funds	
Other investments	
Total investment assets	
Real Estate	
Residence	
Vacation home	
Other	
Total real estate	
Total Assets	

Liabilities and Net Worth

Current Liabilities	
Loans	
Credit card balance	
Other current liabilities	
Total current liabilities	
Long-Term Liabilities	
Mortgage	
Car loan	
Other long-term liabilities	
Total long-term liabilities	
Total Liabilities	

Net Worth	

3. Reevaluate the goals you set in Chapter 1. Based on your personal cash flow statement, indicate how much you can save each year to reach the goals you set.

Personal Financial Goals

Financial Goal	Dollar Amount	Savings per Year	Number of Years
Short-Term Goals			
1.			
2.			
3.			
4.			
5.			
Intermediate-Term Goals			
1.			
2.			
3.			
4.			
5.			
Long-Term Goals			
1.			
2.			
3.			
4.			
5.			

Decisions

1. Describe the actions you will take to increase your net cash flows in the near future.

2. Detail your plans for increasing your net cash flows in the distant future.

Chapter 3: Applying Time Value Concepts

Goals

1. Determine how much savings you will accumulate by various future points in time.
2. Estimate how much you will need to save each year in order to achieve the goals you have set.

Analysis

1. For each goal you set in Chapter 1, make three calculations using an interest rate that you believe you can earn on your invested savings and a rate that is one point higher and one point lower than that rate. (The Excel template will perform the calculations based on your input.)

Time Value of Money

Future Value of a Present Amount	
Present Value	
Number of Periods	
Interest Rate per Period	
Future Value	

Future Value of an Annuity	
Payment per Period	
Number of Periods	
Interest Rate per Period	
Future Value	

Present Value of a Future Amount	
Future Value	
Number of Periods	
Interest Rate per Period	
Present Value	

Present Value of an Annuity	
Payment per Period	
Number of Periods	
Interest Rate per Period	
Present Value	

Personal Financial Goals

Financial Goal	Dollar Amount	Rate of Return	Priority (Low, Medium, High)
Short-Term Goals			
1.			
2.			
3.			
4.			
5.			
Intermediate-Term Goals			
1.			
2.			
3.			
4.			
5.			
Long-Term Goals			
1.			
2.			
3.			
4.			
5.			

2. Revise the cash flow statement you created in Chapter 2 as necessary to enable you to achieve your goals.

Personal Cash Flow Statement

Cash Inflows   **This Month**

    Disposable (after-tax) income   _____

    Interest on deposits   _____

    Dividend payments   _____

    Other   _____

Total Cash Inflows

Cash Outflows

    Rent   _____

    Cable TV   _____

    Electricity and water   _____

    Telephone   _____

    Groceries   _____

    Health care insurance and expenses   _____

    Clothing   _____

    Car expenses (insurance, maintenance, and gas)   _____

    Recreation   _____

    Other   _____

Total Cash Outflows

Net Cash Flows

Decisions

1. Report on how much you must save per year and the return you must earn to meet your goals.

Chapter 4: Using Tax Concepts for Planning

Goals

1. Reduce taxable income (thereby reducing taxes paid) to the extent allowable by the IRS.
2. Reduce taxes paid by deferring income.

Analysis

1. Use the template below to estimate your federal income tax liability based on the 2002 guidelines presented in the text or current tax regulations and rates. (The Excel template will calculate your tax liability based on your input.)

Select one of the following as your Filing Status:
- Single _____
- Married, Filing Joint Return _____
- Married, Filing Separate Return _____
- Head of Household _____
- Qualifying Widow(er) with Dependent Child _____

Your status will determine how you compute your taxes, as shown in Exhibit 4.6 in the text.

Gross Income Computation:			
Salary (After Retirement Contribution)	$		
Interest Income	$		
Dividend Income	$		
Long-term Capital Gain	$		
Short-term Capital Gain	$		
Gross Income		$	
Standard Deduction *(Refer to Exhibit 4.4 in text)*	$		
Itemized Deductions			
Medical Expenses	$		
Minus .075 x Gross Income	$		
Deductible Medical Expenses		$	
State Income Taxes		$	
Real Estate Taxes		$	
Interest Expense		$	
Charitable Donations		$	
Total Itemized Deductions		$	

Enter the Larger of the Total Itemized Deductions or Standard Deduction			$
Exemptions	$3,000	x ___ (number)	$
Taxable Income (Gross Income – Deductions and Exemptions)			$
Tax Liability (*Refer to Exhibit 4.6 in text*)			
Capital Gains Tax			
Long-term Capital Gains	$		
Long-term Capital Gains Tax Rate (*From Exhibit 4.3*)	%		
Capital Gain Tax			$
Your Total Tax Liability (capital gains tax plus tax liability)			$

2. For each of the goals you established in Chapter 1, indicate tax advantage options that may enable you to increase your deductions and/or reduce your gross income.

Personal Financial Goals

Financial Goal	**Dollar Amount**	**Rate of Return**	**Priority (Low, Medium, High)**	**Tax Advantage Options**
Short-Term Goals				
1.				
2.				
3.				
4.				
5.				
Intermediate-Term Goals				
1.				
2.				
3.				
4.				
5.				
Long-Term Goals				
1.				
2.				
3.				
4.				
5.				

3. If you are considering hiring a tax preparer, use the following questions as an interview guide to screen candidates.

Answers

1. How long have you been preparing tax returns?

2. What training have you had in the preparation of tax returns?

    College degrees earned:

    Tax training courses:

    Certifications:

3. How long have you worked for this organization?

4. Do you carry professional liability insurance?

5. Is this your full-time job?

6. If I am audited, are you authorized to represent me before the IRS?

7. How many hours of continuing professional education are you required to have each year to maintain your employment?

8. How many tax returns do you prepare a year?

9. What type of software does your firm use to prepare returns?

10. What percentage of the returns done by you have been audited?

Decisions

1. Describe the actions you will take to achieve tax (i.e., increasing deductions or reducing gross income) savings in the present year.

2. Detail the means by which you will reduce your tax liability in the future (i.e., increasing deductions or reducing gross income).

Chapter 5: Banking and Interest Rates

Goals
1. Identify the banking services that are most important to you.
2. Determine which financial institution will provide you with the best banking services.

Analysis

1. Evaluate what banking services are most important to you with a score of "10" for the most important and "1" for the least. Then evaluate five financial institutions with respect to the services offered; rate the institutions from "5" as the best for that service to "1" as the worst. The template will calculate scores for each institution.

Banking Services Scorecard

SERVICES OFFERED	Priority	Commercial Bank		Savings Institution		Credit Union		INSTITUTION 4		INSTITUTION 5	
		Rank	Score	Rank	Score	Rank	Score	Rank	Score	Rank	Score
1. Hours of operations— evenings, Saturdays											
2. Locations— proximity to work and home											
3. Fees/Minimum balance for checking accounts											
4. Fees for ATM usage											
5. Interest rate on savings accounts											
6. Interest rate on checking accounts											
7. VISA/Master Card available and annual fee											
8. Interest rate on home loans											
9. Interest rate on car loans											
10. Safety deposit boxes and rental rates											
TOTAL SCORE FOR EACH INSTITUTION											

2. In the chart below, enter the amount of money you currently have on deposit or would like to have on deposit next to the appropriate depository account. After you have done this, go to the Web site of two financial institutions and determine the interest rates currently being paid for each of the depository accounts that you have selected and compare the annual returns.

Account Type	Amount on Deposit	INSTITUTION 1		INSTITUTION 2	
		Interest Rate	Total Annual Return	Interest Rate	Total Annual Return
Checking Account					
NOW Account					
Savings Deposit					
CD-6 months					
CD-12 months					
CD-18 months					
CD-24 months					
CD-36 months					
CD-48 months					
CD-60 months					
Money Market Deposit Account					

If you enter this information in the Excel template, the software will create a graphical comparison of the return from each investment.

3. Use the following template as a guide for reconciling your checking account balance by entering data from your bank statement and checkbook register. If the two balances do not match, carefully check your math and records. If there is still a discrepancy, contact the financial institution.

Bank Statement Balance	$	Checkbook Register Balance	$
Plus Deposits in Transit (*Total of deposits that appear in your checkbook but do not appear on the bank statement*)	$	Plus Interest	$
Subtotal	$	Subtotal	$
Minus Outstanding Checks (*Total of any checks that you have written that do not appear on the bank statement; use the below template to aid your computations*)	$	Minus Service Charge	$
Subtotal	$	Subtotal	$
Plus — Other (*Any items that appear in your checkbook but not on the bank statement as well as any error that the bank has made)* Description:	$	Plus — Other (*Including errors in your checkbook*) Description:	$
Minus — Other* Description:	$	Minus — Other (*Including errors in your checkbook*) Description:	$
Reconciled Balance	$	Reconciled Balance	$

* Example: If you have ordered new checks and deducted the amount from your checkbook but the bank has not yet deducted the amount from your account on their records.

Outstanding Checks

CK#	$
CK#	$
CK#	$
CK#	$
CK#	$
CK#	$
CK#	$
CK#	$
CK#	$
Total	**$**

Decisions

1. Describe the services and characteristics that are of prime importance to you in a financial institution.

2. Which of the financial institutions you evaluated is most optimal for your needs? Why?

Chapter 6: Managing Your Money

Goals

1. Maintain sufficient liquidity to ensure that all your anticipated bills are paid on time.
2. Maintain sufficient liquidity so that you can cover unanticipated expenses.
3. Invest any excess funds in deposits that offer the highest return while ensuring liquidity.

Analysis

1. Review the cash flow statement you prepared in Chapter 3 and assess your liquidity.
2. Evaluate the short-term goals you created in Chapter 1 as high, medium, or low with respect to liquidity, risk, fees/minimum balance, and return.

Short-term Goal Prioritization of Factors

Short-Term Goal	Liquidity	Risk	Fees/Minimum Balance	Return

3. Rank each of the money market investments as good, fair, or poor with respect to liquidity, risk, fees/minimum balance, and return.

Money Market Investment	Liquidity	Risk	Fees/Minimum Balance	Return
Checking Account				
NOW Account				
Savings Account				
Money Market Deposit Account (MMDA)				
Certificate of Deposit				
Treasury Bill				
Money Market Fund				
Asset Management Account				

Decisions

1. Describe how you will ensure adequate liquidity to cover anticipated expenses.

2. Detail how you will ensure liquidity to meet unanticipated expenses.

3. Explain which money market investments will be most effective in reaching your short-term goals.

Chapter 7: Managing Your Credit

Goals

1. Evaluate your credit report.
2. Determine your overall creditworthiness.
3. Set a policy to avoid incurring high interest expenses on credit cards by aggressively paying any existing credit card debt and selecting credit cards with competitive interest rates.

Analysis

1. Obtain a copy of your credit report from www.transunion.com or www.creditbase.com, scrutinize the report, and report any inaccuracies to the credit bureaus.

2. Using the MSN homepage, determine your overall creditworthiness. At www.msn.com, click on the tab entitled "Money," and then click on "Planning." When the "Savings and Debt Management" page comes up, go to the section entitled "Debt Evaluator" and follow the instructions.

3. Referring to your personal cash flow statement, determine how much excess cash inflows you have each month. Based on this amount, set a self-imposed credit limit each month so that you can pay your balance off in full. If you have existing credit card debt, use the below template to determine how many months it will take to pay off your balance at three different monthly payment amounts. (The Excel template will perform the calculation for you.) Revise your cash flow statement based on your decisions.

	Alternative 1	*Alternative 2*	*Alternative 3*
Credit Card Debt			
Monthly Payment			
Interest Rate per Year			
Months to Pay Off Debt			

4. Use the following template to select a credit card with favorable terms. Rate the cards from five being the best in an area to one being the worst.

Bank Credit Card Scorecard

Question	Credit Card Issuer				
	1	2	3	4	5
1. Annual fee					
2. Interest rate on purchases					
3. Interest rate on cash advances					
4. Transaction fee for cash advances					
5. Insurance on purchases					
6. Credit earned toward purchases at selected businesses					
7. Frequent flyer miles					
8. Free delivery on mail order purchases					
9. Phone card capability					
10. Credit limit available					
11.					
12.					
13.					
14.					
15.					
Total					

Decisions

1. Are there any errors on your credit report that you must correct? How can you improve your creditworthiness?

2. What is your self-imposed credit each month for future credit card purchases? How much of your cash inflows do you need to allot each month to paying off any existing credit card debt?

3. What credit card offers are the most favorable terms for your needs?

Chapter 8: Personal Loans

Goals

1. Limit your personal financing to a level and maturity that you can pay back on a timely basis.
2. For loans you anticipate needing in the future, evaluate the advantages and disadvantages of lenders.
3. Compare the cost of buying and leasing a car.

Analysis

1. Review your personal cash flow statement. How much can you afford to pay each month for personal loans?
2. Identify several prospective lenders for personal loans you may need in the future. What are the advantages and disadvantages of each source with respect to the interest rates offered, method of calculating interest, and other criteria of importance to you?

Loan Evaluation

Loan One

Description of Loan	Sources for Loan	Advantages of Source	Disadvantages of Source
	1.		
	2.		
	3.		

Loan Two

Description of Loan	Sources for Loan	Advantages of Source	Disadvantages of Source
	1.		
	2.		
	3.		

Loan Three

Description of Loan	Sources for Loan	Advantages of Source	Disadvantages of Source
	1.		
	2.		
	3.		

Loan Four

Description of Loan	Sources for Loan	Advantages of Source	Disadvantages of Source
	1.		
	2.		
	3.		

3. Compare the cost of purchasing a car versus leasing a car over a 4-year period.

Cost of Purchasing versus Leasing a Car

Cost of Purchasing the Car

Down payment   _____

Interest rate   _____

Number of months   _____

Annual forgone interest on down payment   _____

Monthly payment on car loan   _____

Total monthly payments   _____

Total cost of purchasing   _____

Expected amount to be received when car is sold   _____

Total cost of purchasing   _____

Cost of Leasing the Car

Security deposit   _____

Forgone interest   _____

Monthly lease payments   _____

Total monthly payments   _____

Total cost of leasing   _____

If you enter this information in the Excel template, the software will create a graphical comparison of purchasing versus leasing.

Decisions

1. Report how much you can afford to spend each month on personal loans.

2. Report which lenders you may consider using in the future and why.

3. For your needs, is purchasing or leasing a vehicle a better choice?

Chapter 9: Purchasing and Financing a Home

Goals

1. Limit the amount of mortgage financing to an affordable level; determine if homeownership or renting is better financially.
2. Select the shortest loan maturity with affordable monthly payments.
3. Select the mortgage loan type (fixed or adjustable rate) that is most likely to result in the lowest interest expenses.

Analysis

1. The amount of house that a person can afford is affected by many factors. The templates below will help you to determine the impact of interest rates, term of loan, and loan type (i.e., fixed or adjustable rate) on this process. Go to the Web site www.lendingtree.com. Click on "Calculators" located on the bottom left side of the screen. Referring to the personal cash flow statement developed in Chapter 2, use the amount that you determined is available for rent as the basis for the amount of house payment that you can afford each month. By using trial and error on the adjustable and fixed mortgage loan calculators, adjust the amount of mortgage either up or down until the "monthly payment" approximately equals the amount you determined for rent in your cash flow statement. Enter the amount of the mortgage that you can afford in the templates below as well as the amount of the down payment that you have or expect to have when you purchase a house. Repeat the process using the other interest rates and mortgage terms indicated in the worksheets. Remember: Maintain the same "number of months between adjustments," "expected adjustments" and "interest rate cap" for each of the adjustable-rate calculations.

Fixed Rate

Interest Rate	6%
Term	30 Years
Amount of Down Payment	$
Amount of Mortgage	$
Total Price of House (Down Payment Plus Mortgage)	$

Interest Rate	7%
Term	30 Years
Amount of Down Payment	$
Amount of Mortgage	$
Total Price of House (Down Payment Plus Mortgage)	$

Interest Rate	8%
Term	30 Years
Amount of Down Payment	$
Amount of Mortgage	$
Total Price of House (Down Payment Plus Mortgage)	$

Interest Rate	6%
Term	15 Years
Amount of Down Payment	$
Amount of Mortgage	$
Total Price of House (Down Payment Plus Mortgage)	$

Interest Rate	7%
Term	15 Years
Amount of Down Payment	$
Amount of Mortgage	$
Total Price of House (Down Payment Plus Mortgage)	$

Interest Rate	8%
Term	15 Years
Amount of Down Payment	$
Amount of Mortgage	$
Total Price of House (Down Payment Plus Mortgage)	$

Adjustable Rate

Starting interest Rate	6%
Term	15 Years
Months Between Adjustments (not to exceed 12 months)	
Expected Adjustment	
Interest Rate Cap	
Amount of Down Payment	$
Amount of Mortgage	$
Total Price of House (Down Payment Plus Mortgage)	$

Starting interest Rate	7%
Term	15 Years
Months Between Adjustments (not to exceed 12 months)	
Expected Adjustment	
Interest Rate Cap	
Amount of Down Payment	$
Amount of Mortgage	$
Total Price of House (Down Payment Plus Mortgage)	$

Starting interest Rate	8%
Term	15 Years
Months Between Adjustments (not to exceed 12 months)	
Expected Adjustment	
Interest Rate Cap	
Amount of Down Payment	$
Amount of Mortgage	$
Total Price of House (Down Payment Plus Mortgage)	$

Starting interest Rate	6%
Term	30 Years
Months Between Adjustments (not to exceed 12 months)	
Expected Adjustment	
Interest Rate Cap	
Amount of Down Payment	$
Amount of Mortgage	$
Total Price of House (Down Payment Plus Mortgage)	$

Starting interest Rate	7%
Term	30 Years
Months Between Adjustments (not to exceed 12 months)	
Expected Adjustment	
Interest Rate Cap	
Amount of Down Payment	$
Amount of Mortgage	$
Total Price of House (Down Payment Plus Mortgage)	$

Starting interest Rate	8%
Term	30 Years
Months Between Adjustments (not to exceed 12 months)	
Expected Adjustment	
Interest Rate Cap	
Amount of Down Payment	$
Amount of Mortgage	$
Total Price of House (Down Payment Plus Mortgage)	$

2. At www.msn.com, search listings of homes for sale in your price range by clicking on "House and Home" on the right side of the screen and then on "Buying a House." Complete the information requested under ""Compare and Find Homes" to research cities and neighborhoods that you are interested in. Record information on homes of interest below.

	From	To
Price Range:		
Zip Code:		

Potential Homes

Address	List Price	MSN Price Estimate	Monthly Payment	Realtor

3. Referring to your cash flow statement and personal balance sheet, compare the monthly payment estimates to the amount of money you are currently paying for rent. Determine the amount of a down payment you can afford to make.

Down payment $_____

4. At www.msn.com, click on "House and Home" on the right side of the screen and then on "Research Online Loans" at the lower left side of the page. Gather current information on loan rates and record it below.

Mortgage Type	Rate

5. Create an amortization table for the fixed-rate mortgage that is most affordable. (The Excel template will calculate the monthly payment based on your input and create the amortization table.)

Loan Amount   _____

Number of Years   _____

Annual Interest Rate   _____

Monthly Payment   _____

Amortization Schedule for Year 1

Monthly Payment	Payment	Principal	Interest	Balance

Compare the allocation of principal versus interest paid per year on the loan. (The Excel template will create a bar graph based on your input.)

Amortization Schedule (Annual Totals)

Annual Payments	Total Payments	Principal	Interest	Balance
1				
2				
3				
4				
5				
6				
7				
8				
9				
10				
11				
12				
13				
14				
15				
16				
17				
18				
19				
20				
21				
22				
23				
24				
25				
26				
27				
28				
29				
30				
31				
32				
33				
34				
35				
36				
37				
38				
39				
40				

6. Select the mortgage with the best terms. Compare the cost of buying a home with these mortgage terms to renting over a 3-year period.

Renting Versus Owning a Home

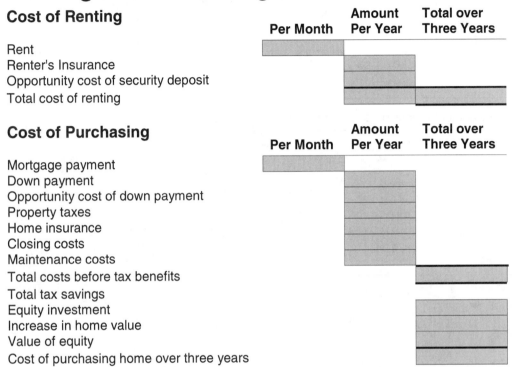

Cost of Renting

	Per Month	Amount Per Year	Total over Three Years
Rent			
Renter's Insurance			
Opportunity cost of security deposit			
Total cost of renting			

Cost of Purchasing

	Per Month	Amount Per Year	Total over Three Years
Mortgage payment			
Down payment			
Opportunity cost of down payment			
Property taxes			
Home insurance			
Closing costs			
Maintenance costs			
Total costs before tax benefits			
Total tax savings			
Equity investment			
Increase in home value			
Value of equity			
Cost of purchasing home over three years			

If you enter this information in the Excel template, the software will create a chart comparing the cost of renting to purchasing.

Decisions

1. What is the mortgage amount and down payment that you can afford?

2. Is a fixed-rate or adjustable-rate mortgage better suited to your financial situation? What maturity, interest rate, and monthly payment can you afford?

3. Describe whether homeownership or renting is preferable for you.

Chapter 10: Auto and Homeowner's Insurance

Goals

1. Ensure that your car and dwelling are adequately insured.
2. Prepare a home inventory.
3. Determine whether you should increase your auto and homeowner's/rental insurance in the future.

Analysis

1. Review the personal balance sheet you created in Chapter 2. Which assets require coverage from an auto or homeowner's/rental policy? What risks should you insure against?

2. Using Web sites such as www.insurance.com and www.insweb.com, obtain three quotes from three separate companies for automobile insurance. Have information on hand for the year, make, and model of your vehicle and estimates for how many miles you drive per year. Base the quotations on the limits of liability listed (e.g., bodily injury limit of $100,000/ $300,000 limit). Insert the deductible you desire in the respective blanks on the form (and be sure to maintain same deductibles for all quotes). Input the information from each quote in the below templates to aid your comparison of the various policies.

Company A: _____

COVERAGE

Liability		
Bodily Injury ($100,000/$300,000 limit)	$	
Property Damage ($50,000 limit)	$	
Subtotal Liability		$
No-fault Medical Expenses and Income Loss	$	
Uninsured/Underinsured Motorist ($100,000/$300,000 limit)	$	
Collision ($_____ Deductible)	$	
Comprehensive ($_____ Deductible)	$	
Emergency Road Service	$	
Subtotal		$
Additional Charges (List):	$	
	$	
	$	
	$	
	$	
	$	
Subtotal		$
Discounts in the Premium		
Anti-lock Brakes	$	
Accident-free Last 7 Years	$	
Other Discounts (List):	$	
	$	
	$	
	$	
	$	
Minus Total Discounts		$
Total Amount Due		$

Company B: _____

COVERAGE

Liability		
Bodily Injury ($100,000/$300,000 limit)	$	
Property Damage ($50,000 limit)	$	
Subtotal Liability		$
No-fault Medical Expenses and Income Loss	$	
Uninsured/Underinsured Motorist ($100,000/$300,000 limit)	$	
Collision ($_____ Deductible)	$	
Comprehensive ($_____ Deductible)	$	
Emergency Road Service	$	
Subtotal		$
Additional Charges (List):	$	
	$	
	$	
	$	
	$	
	$	
Subtotal		$
Discounts in the Premium		
Anti-lock Brakes	$	
Accident-free Last 7 Years	$	
Other Discounts (List):	$	
	$	
	$	
	$	
	$	
Minus Total Discounts		$
Total Amount Due		$

Company C: _____

COVERAGE

Liability		
Bodily Injury ($100,000/$300,000 limit)	$	
Property Damage ($50,000 limit)	$	
Subtotal Liability		$
No-fault Medical Expenses and Income Loss	$	
Uninsured/Underinsured Motorist ($100,000/$300,000 limit)	$	
Collision ($_____ Deductible)	$	
Comprehensive ($_____ Deductible)	$	
Emergency Road Service	$	
Subtotal		$
Additional Charges (List):	$	
	$	
	$	
	$	
	$	
	$	
Subtotal		$
Discounts in the Premium		
Anti-lock Brakes	$	
Accident-free Last 7 Years	$	
Other Discounts (List):	$	
	$	
	$	
	$	
	$	
Minus Total Discounts		$
Total Amount Due		$

3. Complete your home inventory using the below template. If you input this information in the Excel template, the software will perform calculations and present pie charts showing the purchase cost of your property versus the replacement cost. Based on your inventory, how much personal property coverage should you have? Is replacement costs or cash value a better policy option? Do you need a personal property floater for any high-ticket items?

In addition to facilitating the process of settling insurance claims and verifying losses, a home inventory helps you to determine the amount of insurance you need. The complexity of your inventory will depend upon your stage in life and family situation. It's a good idea to include copies of sales receipts and purchase contracts with your inventory. After completing your home inventory, print out multiple copies and file them in secure locations (safety deposit box, fireproof box, at your parent's home, etc.). You should also consider taking pictures of individual items or videotaping entire rooms as further documentation.

Home Inventory

	Item Description	Make And Model	Date Acquired	Estimated Purchase Cost	Estimated Replacement Cost
Electronics					
Computer Equipment					
Television					
Stereo Equipment					
DVD/VCR					
Cellular Phone/Pager					
Camera/Video Camera					
Major Appliances					
Refrigerator/Freezer					
Stove					
Washer/Dryer					
Microwave					
Coffee Maker					
Vacuum					
Blender/Food Processor					
Clothing and Accessories					
Pants					
Shirts					
Sweaters					
Coats					
Dresses					
Skirts					
Shoes					
Accessories (belts, ties, etc.)					
Watches					
Rings					
Earrings					
Necklaces					
Bracelets					
Cufflinks					
Linens					
Towels					
Bedding					

Home Inventory (continued)

	Item Description	Make And Model	Date Acquired	Estimated Purchase Cost	Estimated Replacement Cost
Furniture					
Living Room Set					
Dining Room Set					
Bedroom Sets					
Kitchen Set					
Bookshelves					
Lamps					
Rugs					
Art and Music					
Books					
CDs/Records/Audio Tapes					
DVD/VCR Tapes					
Artwork					
Kitchen Equipment					
Dishes					
Glassware					
Silverware					
Pots and Pans					
Utensils					
Athletic Equipment					
Collectibles					
Other					

4. Using the following Web sites, obtain quotes for your homeowner's or renter's insurance policy. After obtaining the quotes, complete the worksheets below to aid your comparison of policies. Note: Some of these Web sites will provide you with a quote online while others will indicate that a quote will be sent to you via U.S. mail or other medium. Insert the deductible you desire on the form (and be sure to maintain the same deductible for all quotes).

Web sites:
   www.amica.com
   www.val-u-web.com/house.htm
   www.savvy-bargains.com/insurance/homeowner-insurance-quote.html
   www.homeownerswiz.com/
   www.quotefetcher.com/home-insurance.htm

Company A _____

Coverage and Limits

Dwelling	$
Personal Property ($_____ deductible)	$
Personal Liability	$
Damage to Property of Others	$
Medical Payments to Others (per person)	$
Discounts	$
Annual Premium	$

Company B _____

Coverage and Limits

Dwelling	$
Personal Property ($_____ deductible)	$
Personal Liability	$
Damage to Property of Others	$
Medical Payments to Others (per person)	$
Discounts	$
Annual Premium	$

Company C _____

Coverage and Limits

Dwelling	$
Personal Property ($_____ deductible)	$
Personal Liability	$
Damage to Property of Others	$
Medical Payments to Others (per person)	$
Discounts	$
Annual Premium	$

Decisions

1. What are the key risks related to auto and homeowner's insurance that you will insure against?

2. What coverage levels will you maintain for your auto policy? Which of the policy quotes you requested is most attractive? What actions can you take to receive policy discounts in the future?

3. What coverage levels will you maintain for your homeowner's policy? Which of the policy quotes you requested is most attractive? What actions can you take to receive policy discounts in the future?

Chapter 11: Health Insurance

Goals

1. Ensure that your health and disability insurance adequately protects your wealth.
2. Develop a plan for your future health insurance needs, including long-term care.

Analysis

1. Complete the following worksheet to aid your evaluation of information provided by your employer for your health insurance options. Which type of policy (indemnity plan, HMO, or PPO) is best suited to your needs and budget?

HEALTH INSURANCE COVERAGE COMPARISON

Indemnity Plan

Premium Co-pays	☐ Yes ☐ No
If Yes, Amount of Premium Co-pays	$
Coverage Eligibility	☐ Self ☐ 2-person ☐ Family
Coverage:	
In State	☐ Yes ☐ No
Out of State	☐ Yes ☐ No
Out of the Country	☐ Yes ☐ No
Prescription Coverage	☐ Yes ☐ No
If Yes, Amount of Co-pay	$
Office Visits:	
Co-pay Amount	$
Annual Deductible	☐ Yes ☐ No
If Yes, Amount of Deductible	$
Hospital Benefits:	
Maximum Days of Hospital Care	_____ Days
Maximum Days for Mental Health or	
Substance Abuse	_____ Days
Co-pay	☐ Yes ☐ No
If Yes, Amount of Co-pay	$
Annual Deductible	☐ Yes ☐ No
If Yes, Amount of Deductible	$
Outpatient Care:	
Emergency Room Care	☐ Yes ☐ No
Physical Therapy	☐ Yes ☐ No
Occupational Therapy	☐ Yes ☐ No
Speech Therapy	☐ Yes ☐ No

Dental Coverage:	☐ Yes	☐ No
If Yes, Co-pays for Regular Checkups	☐ Yes	☐ No
If Yes, How Much	$	
Orthodontic Coverage:	☐ Yes	☐ No
If Yes, Co-pays for Regular Checkups	☐ Yes	☐ No
If Yes, How Much	$	
Vision Coverage:	☐ Yes	☐ No
Frequency of Regular Eye Exams	_____	
Co-pay for Regular Eye Exams	$	
Frequency for New Lenses	_____	
Co-pay for New Lenses	$	
Frequency for New Frames	_____	
Co-pay for New Frames	$	

HMO

Premium Co-pays	☐ Yes	☐ No	
If Yes, Amount of Premium Co-pays	$		
Coverage Eligibility	☐ Self	☐ 2-person	☐ Family
Coverage:			
In State	☐ Yes	☐ No	
Out of State	☐ Yes	☐ No	
Out of the Country	☐ Yes	☐ No	
Prescription Coverage	☐ Yes	☐ No	
If Yes, Amount of Co-pay	$		
Office Visits:			
Co-pay Amount	$		
Annual Deductible	☐ Yes	☐ No	
If Yes, Amount of Deductible	$		
Hospital Benefits:			
Maximum Days of Hospital Care	_____Days		
Maximum Days for Mental Health or Substance Abuse	_____Days		
Co-pay	☐ Yes	☐ No	
If Yes, Amount of Co-pay	$		
Annual Deductible	☐ Yes	☐ No	
If Yes, Amount of Deductible	$		
Outpatient Care:			
Emergency Room Care	☐ Yes	☐ No	
Physical Therapy	☐ Yes	☐ No	
Occupational Therapy	☐ Yes	☐ No	
Speech Therapy	☐ Yes	☐ No	

Dental Coverage:	☐ Yes ☐ No
If Yes, Co-pays for Regular	
Checkups	☐ Yes ☐ No
If Yes, How Much	$
Orthodontic Coverage:	☐ Yes ☐ No
If Yes, Co-pays for Regular	
Checkups	☐ Yes ☐ No
If Yes, How Much	$
Vision Coverage:	☐ Yes ☐ No
Frequency of Regular Eye Exams	_____
Co-pay for Regular Eye Exams	$
Frequency for New Lenses	_____
Co-pay for New Lenses	$
Frequency for New Frames	_____
Co-pay for New Frames	$

PPO

Premium Co-pays	☐ Yes ☐ No
If Yes, Amount of Premium Co-pays	$
Coverage Eligibility	☐ Self ☐ 2-person ☐ Family
Coverage:	
In State	☐ Yes ☐ No
Out of State	☐ Yes ☐ No
Out of the Country	☐ Yes ☐ No
Prescription Coverage	☐ Yes ☐ No
If Yes, Amount of Co-pay	$
Office Visits:	
Co-pay Amount	$
Annual Deductible	☐ Yes ☐ No
If Yes, Amount of Deductible	$
Hospital Benefits:	
Maximum Days of Hospital Care	_____Days
Maximum Days for Mental Health or	
Substance Abuse	_____Days
Co-pay	☐ Yes ☐ No
If Yes, Amount of Co-pay	$
Annual Deductible	☐ Yes ☐ No
If Yes, Amount of Deductible	$
Outpatient Care:	
Emergency Room Care	☐ Yes ☐ No
Physical Therapy	☐ Yes ☐ No
Occupational Therapy	☐ Yes ☐ No
Speech Therapy	☐ Yes ☐ No

Dental Coverage:	☐ Yes	☐ No
If Yes, Co-pays for Regular		
Checkups	☐ Yes	☐ No
If Yes, How Much	$	
Orthodontic Coverage:	☐ Yes	☐ No
If Yes, Co-pays for Regular		
Checkups	☐ Yes	☐ No
If Yes, How Much	$	
Vision Coverage:	☐ Yes	☐ No
Frequency of Regular Eye Exams	_____	
Co-pay for Regular Eye Exams	$	
Frequency for New Lenses	_____	
Co-pay for New Lenses	$	
Frequency for New Frames	_____	
Co-pay for New Frames	$	

2. If you are under age 60, long-term care insurance has probably not been a major concern to date. Based on your family health history, your financial situation, and any long-term illnesses that you have, should you look into getting a policy? Why or why not?

[ ]

3. Referring to the personal cash flow statement you developed in Chapter 2 of this workbook, complete the following template to determine your disability insurance needs. (If you input this information in the Excel template, the software will create a chart showing your sources of disability income.)

DISABILITY INSURANCE NEEDS

Cash Inflows	$	
Minus Work Related Cash Inflows*	$	
Cash Inflows if Disabled		$
Total Cash Outflows	$	
Minus Work-Related Cash Outflows*	$	
Cash Outflows if Disabled		$
Cash Inflows Minus Outflows – Net Cash Flows if Disabled		$
Employer Disability Insurance	$	
Social Security	$	
Workmen's Compensation	$	
Total Insurance Cash Inflows		$
Net Cash Flows if Disabled Minus Total Insurance Cash Inflows**		$

* Cash flows that will discontinue if you are not working.

** A negative number indicates the amount of disability insurance coverage that you need per month. However, if the number is positive it indicates that you have no need for disability insurance.

Decisions

1. What steps have you taken or will you take to ensure that your health insurance needs are being met? Which type of health insurance plan will you seek from an employer?

2. Does your age, personal health history, or family health history indicate that you should consider long-term care insurance?

3. What are your disability insurance needs? What amount of additional coverage, if any, do you require?

Chapter 12: Life Insurance

Goals

1. Determine whether you need to purchase life insurance and if so, how much.
2. Determine the most appropriate types of life insurance.
3. Decide whether you should purchase or add to life insurance in the future.

Analysis

1. Your life insurance needs are dependent upon several factors. The template below employs the budget method discussed in the text to determine the amount of insurance that you need. Complete the worksheet by filling in the appropriate information to determine your life insurance needs.

1.	Annual living expenses (*Refer to your personal cash flow statement developed in Chapter 2 to determine this figure.*)	$		
2.	Minus spouse's disposable "after-tax" income	$		
3.	Minus interest or dividends from savings*	$		
4.	Minus other income	$		
5.	Annual living expenses to be replaced by insurance (line 1 minus lines 2, 3 and 4)		$	
6.	Assuming a 6% rate of return and the number of years of expenses for which you will need coverage, determine the present value. (Line 5 times PVIFA for _____ years at 6%)		X _____	
7.	Insurance needs for annual living expenses (line 5 times line 6)			$
8.	Special future expenses		$	
9.	Determine the number of years until line 8 above occurs and multiply by the present value of a dollar assuming 6% (line 8 times PVIF _____ years at 6%)		X _____	

10. Insurance needs for special future expenses (line 8 times line 9)		$
11. Current debt to be repaid by insurance proceeds		$
12. Educational/training expenses for spouse to be paid by insurance proceeds		$
13. Value of existing savings		$
14. Final expenses (*Funeral and other related items*)		$
15. Life insurance provided by employer		$
Total Insurance Needs (Add lines 7, 10, 11,12 and 14 and subtract lines 13 and 15)		$

* This number should be adjusted if savings are to be liquidated and included in box 13 below. Only the interest and dividends from those savings not counted in box 13 should be included here.

2. Review the following information about types of life insurance plans. Indicate how suitable each type is for your situation in the right-hand column.

Type of Insurance Plan	Benefits	Suitability
Term Insurance	Insurance benefits provided to beneficiary	
Whole-Life Insurance	Insurance benefits provided to beneficiary and policy builds a cash value over time	
Universal Insurance	Insurance benefits provided to beneficiary and policy builds a cash value over time	

3. If you have determined that you need life insurance, obtain premiums for the policy type and amount you desire at www.prudential.com. At that site click on the "Products & Services" tab. At the "Tools & Calculators" section on the right side of screen, click on "Insurance Tools." Click on "Life Insurance Quotes" toward the bottom of page. Enter the premiums in the below template.

Policy Type			
Name of Insurance Company			
Total Premium	$	$	$

4. Make any necessary changes to your personal cash flow statement to reflect premiums for life insurance.

Personal Cash Flow Statement

	This Month
Cash Inflows	
Disposable (after-tax) income	_____
Interest on deposits	_____
Dividend payments	_____
Other	_____
Total Cash Inflows	_____
Cash Outflows	
Rent	_____
Cable TV	_____
Electricity and water	_____
Telephone	_____
Groceries	_____
Health care insurance and expenses	_____
Clothing	_____
Car expenses (insurance, maintenance, and gas)	_____
Recreation	_____
Other	_____
Total Cash Outflows	_____
Net Cash Flows	_____

Decisions

1. Do you need life insurance? If so, how much and what type of policy will suit your needs?

2. What do you anticipate your life insurance coverage needs to be in the future?

Chapter 13: Investing Fundamentals

Goals

1. Determine whether to invest, given your current cash flows.
2. Determine what kinds of investments you should purchase to meet your financial goals.

Analysis

1. Review your cash flow statement to determine how much you can afford to invest in stocks each month.
2. Evaluate your risk tolerance to see if your temperament is suited to the uncertainty of stock investments.

Risk Tolerance Quiz

Answer True or False by entering an X in the appropriate box.
(The Excel template will offer an assessment based on your input.)

	TRUE	FALSE

1. If I own stock, I will check its price at least daily if not more often.

2. When driving on an interstate, and traffic and weather permit, I never drive in excess of the posted speed limit.

3. If the price of my stock declines, my first reaction is to sell.

4. Another stock market crash similar to 1929 could occur very unexpectedly.

5. When I fly in less than perfect weather, I tend to get nervous and concerned about my safety.

6. If I sold a stock at a loss of more than 25%, it would greatly shake my confidence in my ability to invest.

7. I intensely dislike blind dates.

8. When I travel, I write down a packing list to be sure that I don't forget anything.

9. When traveling with others, I prefer to do the driving.

10. Before buying a bond I would want to talk to at least two other people to confirm my choice.

Results

0–3 True: You have the risk tolerance to invest in individual common stocks.

4–6 True: You would be a nervous investor, but with more knowledge and a few successes, you could probably raise your risk tolerance to a suitable level. Mutual funds might prove a good starting point for your level of risk tolerance.

7–10 True: You are a very conservative and risk-intolerant investor that is probably better suited to a bond portfolio.

3. Determine whether investments will help you to achieve your short-term, intermediate-term, and long-term goals. Complete the template below for the short-, intermediate-, and long-term goals that you have established and reviewed throughout the course. In determining whether is suitable for each goal, take into consideration the timeline for accomplishing the goal, the critical nature of the goal, and, of course, the results of your risk tolerance test. For those goals that you determine investments are not suitable for, enter an "N" in column three, and do not complete the rest of the line for that goal. If, however, you enter a "Y" in column three, think about the kind of investment that is appropriate and justify your selection of stocks as a risk-appropriate means to accomplish this goal.

Short-Term Goals	Suitable? Yes or No	Type of Investment	Justification
1.			
2.			
3.			
4.			
5.			

Intermediate-Term Goals	Suitable? Yes or No	Type of Investment	Justification
1.			
2.			
3.			
4.			
5.			

Long-Term Goals	Suitable? Yes or No	Type of Investment	Justification
1.			
2.			
3.			
4.			
5.			

Decisions

1. Summarize your reasoning for either investing or not investing to meet your goals.

2. If you decide to invest, how much will you invest each month? What types of investments will you purchase? Why?

Chapter 14: Analysis and Valuation of Stocks

Goals

1. Determine how to value a stock based on information about the economy and the firm.

Analysis

1. Select a stock in which you are considering investing.
2. Go to Web site www.federalreserve.gov/FOMC/BeigeBook/2002. Click on the most current report indicated and read the summary. As you do so, keep in mind the product, and/or service, provided by the company you have selected to analyze. In the space provided below, record your analysis of the Beige Book's economic analysis and its impact on your stock.

Comments

3. Go to the Web site www.smartmoney.com. Click on "Funds" and then roll down to "Fund Snapshots." At the center of the page you will see a box that says "Enter Symbol or Name." Enter the name or symbol of the company you wish to analyze and hit "GO." This will bring up the "Snapshot" tab for your company. Answer the following questions, finding the data in the tab indicated:

Snapshot

(1) Is the price of your stock currently close to its 52-week high or 52-week low? _____

(2) Does this stock pay a dividend and, if so, how much? _____

Charting

(3) What has been the long-term price trend of your company's stock?

News

(4) Do you see any significant news events that may favorably or unfavorably affect your stock?

```


```

Earnings

(5) How well has your company met its earnings estimates?

```


```

(6) How does your company's estimated growth for the current and next fiscal year compare to industry projections?

```


```

(7) How does your company's estimated growth for the current and next fiscal year compare to the S&P 500?

```


```

(8) How does your company's estimated three-five year annual growth compare to the industry projections?

```


```

(9) How does your company's estimated three–five year annual growth compare to the S&P 500?

```


```

Ratings

(10) How many Wall Street analysts rate your stock? _____

(11) What has been the net change in recommendation? _____

(12) How many rate your stock as a:

Strong buy   _____
Moderate buy   _____
Hold   _____
Moderate sell   _____
Strong sell   _____

(13) How do the recommendations for your stock compare to others in the industry?

Competition

(14) How does your company compare, in terms of market value, to its competition, i.e., is it one of the larger or smaller companies in its industry?

(15) How does your company's net profit margin compare to that to its competition, i.e., is it one of the larger or smaller companies in its industry?

(16) How does your company's net profit margin compare to that of its competition?

Key Ratios

(17) How does your company's return on equity compare to that of the industry?

(18) How does your company's assets compare to that of the industry?

Financials

(19) How does the growth in revenues of your company compare to that of its competition?

```




```

(20) How does the growth in net earnings of your company compare to that of its competition?

```




```

Insiders

(21) In analyzing any stock, it is always good to know what the "insiders" are doing. From the chart, are they buying, selling, intending to buy, or doing nothing?

```




```

Summary

(22) Based on your analysis of the above, answer the following questions:

    1. Would this stock be considered a(n) (enter an *X* to signify your choice):

        Growth stock _____

        Income stock _____

    Growth/income stock _____

    2. For which of the intermediate or long-term goals that you established in Chapter 1 would this stock be a suitable investment, if any?

Intermediate-Term Goals	Suitable? Yes or No	Rationale for Selection
1.		
2.		
3.		
4.		
5.		

Long-Term Goals	Suitable? Yes or No	Rationale for Selection
1.		
2.		
3.		
4.		
5.		

Decisions

1. Based on your valuation, will you purchase this stock?

2. If you invest in this particular stock, which of your financial goals will the investment be aimed at achieving?

Chapter 15: Investing in Stocks

Goals

1. Determine a method to use for investing in stocks.

Analysis

1. Answer each of the following questions by checking the box to the right of "Yes" or "No."

A.	I will feel better if I have a specific person to talk to about my account.	☐ Yes ☐ No
B.	I will require professional research assistance to make investment decisions.	☐ Yes ☐ No
C.	I will utilize banking-type services such as check writing and debit cards.	☐ Yes ☐ No
D.	I will feel more comfortable if I have a broker who calls me from time to time with suggestions to improve the performance of my portfolio.	☐ Yes ☐ No
E.	I have a relatively complex portfolio that includes an after-tax account, Roth and/or traditional IRAs and rollover IRAs.	☐ Yes ☐ No
F.	I use my portfolio to meet a variety of goals with varying time horizons (short, intermediate, and long term).	☐ Yes ☐ No
G.	I require advice on the tax implications of my investments.	☐ Yes ☐ No
H.	My portfolio is large enough to require an annual review and rebalancing.	☐ Yes ☐ No
I.	I sleep better if I know who is watching my money.	☐ Yes ☐ No
J.	I feel better doing business with people who know my name.	☐ Yes ☐ No

If you answered "Yes" to five or more of the above questions, you should seriously consider a full-service broker. If you answered "Yes" to less than 5, we suggest you use an online/discount broker.

2. Use the following template as a guide to comparing three potential online or discount brokerage companies.

	Company 1 _____	Company 2 _____	Company 3 _____
Cost per trade	$	$	$
Available investments: Common stocks	☐ Yes ☐ No	☐ Yes ☐ No	☐ Yes ☐ No
Preferred stocks	☐ Yes ☐ No	☐ Yes ☐ No	☐ Yes ☐ No
Corporate bonds	☐ Yes ☐ No	☐ Yes ☐ No	☐ Yes ☐ No
Municipal bonds	☐ Yes ☐ No	☐ Yes ☐ No	☐ Yes ☐ No
Options	☐ Yes ☐ No	☐ Yes ☐ No	☐ Yes ☐ No
Commodities	☐ Yes ☐ No	☐ Yes ☐ No	☐ Yes ☐ No
Annuities	☐ Yes ☐ No	☐ Yes ☐ No	☐ Yes ☐ No
Mutual funds (load)	☐ Yes ☐ No	☐ Yes ☐ No	☐ Yes ☐ No
Mutual funds (no load)	☐ Yes ☐ No	☐ Yes ☐ No	☐ Yes ☐ No
Money Markets	☐ Yes ☐ No	☐ Yes ☐ No	☐ Yes ☐ No
Navigability of Web site			
Phone access to account information			
Real-time portfolio updating			
Minimum initial investment			
Availability of banking features (e.g., credit cards and checks)			
Research tools available			

	Company 1 (cont'd) _____	**Company 2 (cont'd)** _____	**Company 3 (cont'd)** _____
Accounts available: Brokerage account	☐ Yes ☐ No $___ Maint. Fee	☐ Yes ☐ No $___ Maint. Fee	☐ Yes ☐ No $___ Maint. Fee
Traditional IRA	☐ Yes ☐ No $___ Maint. Fee	☐ Yes ☐ No $___ Maint. Fee	☐ Yes ☐ No $___ Maint. Fee
Roth IRA	☐ Yes ☐ No $___ Maint. Fee	☐ Yes ☐ No $___ Maint. Fee	☐ Yes ☐ No $___ Maint. Fee
Rollover IRA	☐ Yes ☐ No $___ Maint. Fee	☐ Yes ☐ No $___ Maint. Fee	☐ Yes ☐ No $___ Maint. Fee
College savings accounts	☐ Yes ☐ No $___ Maint. Fee	☐ Yes ☐ No $___ Maint. Fee	☐ Yes ☐ No $___ Maint. Fee
Referral service to independent financial advisors	☐ Yes ☐ No	☐ Yes ☐ No	☐ Yes ☐ No
Record keeping services	☐ Yes ☐ No	☐ Yes ☐ No	☐ Yes ☐ No
Extended hours trading service	☐ Yes ☐ No	☐ Yes ☐ No	☐ Yes ☐ No

3. If you decide to rely on a full service broker, use the following questions as an interview guide when screening prospective advisors.

Question	Broker 1	Broker 2	Broker 3
1. How long have you been with this firm?			
2. How long have you been in the brokerage business?			
3. What is the average size of the portfolios of your clients?			
4. What is the average cost of a 100-share transaction? (This question will lead to an explanation of the firm's fee structure.)			
5. Does your firm sell no-load mutual funds?			
6. What is the annual maintenance fee for an IRA?			
7. Can I access my account and execute transactions on-line?			
8. Does your firm have services such as check writing, debit card, etc. available?			
9. How many offices does your firm have around the country?			
10. How often do I get statements on my account?			
11. What is the current rate paid on your money market accounts?			
12. What are the typical account fees?			
13.			
14.			
15.			
16.			

Add to this list any questions that are unique to your investing situation and delete any that do not pertain to you

4. What type of orders—market, limit, or buy stop—do you intend to use when purchasing stock? Do you intend to pay with cash or buy on margin? Why?

Decisions

1. What type of brokerage firm will you work with—full-service or discount/online? Why?

2. Summarize your decision on the type of orders you will place to purchase stock and your preference for using cash versus buying on margin.

Chapter 16: Investing in Bonds

Goals

1. Determine if you could benefit from investing in bonds.
2. If you decide to invest in bonds, determine what strategy to use.

Analysis

1. Go to the SmartMoney Web site www.smartmoney.com and click on "Economy and Bonds." This will bring you to a page on bond investing that contains numerous articles that you should review to determine if bonds are suitable for your portfolio considering your financial goals. Review these articles in detail, particularly the one entitled *A Bond Primer*.
2. Go to the Web site www.investinginbonds.com. Click on "Investor's Checklist" located under "Features" on left-hand side of the screen. Answer the basic questions given and review the perspective to the right of each question.

After completing your visits to the Web sites above, carefully consider whether any of your financial goals could be met with bond investing. Indicate the bond type (Treasury, corporate, municipal, government agency) and maturity.

Short-Term Goals	Use Bonds? Yes or No	Type of Bond	Maturity (Years)	Reasoning (factoring in risk exposure)
1.				
2.				
3.				
4.				
5.				

Intermediate-Term Goals	Use Bonds? Yes or No	Type of Bond	Maturity (Years)	Reasoning (factoring in risk exposure)
1.				
2.				
3.				
4.				
5.				

Long-Term Goals	Use Bonds? Yes or No	Type of Bond	Maturity (Years)	Reasoning (factoring in risk exposure)
1.				
2.				
3.				
4.				
5.				

3. Consider the suitability of the following bond investment strategies for your financial situation. Enter your conclusions in the right-hand column.

Strategy to Invest in Bonds	Opinion
1. Interest Rate Strategy	
2. Passive Strategy	
3. Maturity Matching Strategy	

4. Review your personal cash flow statement. If you decide bonds are a good investment, allocate money for them.

Personal Cash Flow Statement

	This Month
Cash Inflows	
Disposable (after-tax) income	_____
Interest on deposits	_____
Dividend payments	_____
Other	_____
Total Cash Inflows	_____
Cash Outflows	
Rent	_____
Cable TV	_____
Electricity and water	_____
Telephone	_____
Groceries	_____
Health care insurance and expenses	_____
Clothing	_____
Car expenses (insurance, maintenance, and gas)	_____
Recreation	_____
Other	_____
Total Cash Outflows	_____
Net Cash Flows	_____

Decisions

1. Describe your rationale for investing or not investing in bonds.

2. If you decide to invest in bonds, what strategy will you use?

Chapter 17: Investing in Mutual Funds

Goals

1. Determine if and how you could benefit from investing in mutual funds.
2. If you decide to invest in mutual funds, choose the best types of funds for your needs.

Analysis

1. At www.smartmoney.com, click on the tab marked "Funds." Under the heading "Tools and Research" located towards the lower left side of the page, click on "Fund Portfolio Builder." Choose two to three that meet your goal needs. Enter your findings in the following chart:

Type of Stock Mutual Funds	Suitable Investment Option?	Reasoning
Growth		
Capital Appreciation		
Equity Income		
Balance Growth and Income		
Sector		
Technology		
Index		
International		

Type of Bond Mutual Fund	Suitable Investment Option?	Reasoning
Treasury		
Ginnie Mae		
Corporate Bond		
High-Yield Bond		
Municipal Bond		
Index Bond		
International Bond		

2. Return to www.smartmoney.com. Click on the tab marked "Funds," then roll down to "More." Next, click on "Best & Worst" located on the right-hand side of screen. Under the Top 25 funds, select the category of funds you identified as meeting one or more of your goals from the pull-down menu. Answer the following questions and note other pertinent information about your fund:

(1) On the "snap-shot" tab, what is the risk versus return relationship for your fund?

(2) On the "return" tab, how does your fund's return compare to the return for its category over various time spans?

(3) On the "expense" tab, what are the expenses for your fund?

(4) How do your fund's expenses compare to the expenses for this category?

(5) Under the "purchase" tab, is this fund open to new investors?

(6) If so, what is the minimum purchase?

(7) What is the minimum subsequent purchase?

(8) Under the "portfolio" tab, how long has the fund manager been in place?

Decisions

1. What is your decision regarding mutual funds? Why are they/aren't they a good investment for you?

2. If you decide to invest in mutual funds, what types of funds will you select? Why?

Chapter 18: Asset Allocation

Goals

1. Ensure that your current asset allocation is appropriate.
2. Determine a plan for future allocation.

Analysis

1. Enter information about your current investments in the following chart. (If you input this information in the Excel template, the software will create a pie chart showing the market value of each investment.)

Type of Investment	Market Value of Investment	Goal(s) Met by Investment and Duration of Goal	Percentage of Funds Allocated to this Investment*
Checking Account			
Savings Account			
CD's			
Money Market			
Mutual Fund — Large Cap			
Mutual Fund — Small Cap			
Mutual Fund — International			
Mutual Fund — Corporate Bonds			
Mutual Fund — Gov't Bonds			
REIT's			
Large Cap Stock			
Small Cap Stock			
International Stock (ADR's)			
Equity in Home			
Other Real Estate Holdings			
Investment in Collectibles (e.g., Antiques, Firearms, Art)			

Type of Investment	Market Value of Investment	Goal(s) Met by Investment and Duration of Goal	Percentage of Funds Allocated to this Investment*
Other Investment _____			
Other Investment _____			
Other Investment _____			
Other Investment _____			
Total Investments			

* To compute the percentage manually, take the dollar amount in the "Market Value Investment" column for each type of investment and divide it by the dollar amount for "Total Investments."

2. Referring to Exhibit 18.7 in the textbook, how would you rate your portfolio, (i.e., conservative, moderate, or aggressive)?

```



```

3. Does the risk level of your portfolio correspond to your personal risk tolerance (refer to the risk tolerance quiz in Chapter 13 of this workbook)? If it does not correspond, what actions will you need to take to align the risk level of your portfolio and your own personal risk tolerance?

```



```

Decisions

1. Is your current asset allocation appropriate? If not, what changes will you make to better diversify your investments?

2. As you make additional investments in the future, how do you plan on allocating your assets?

Chapter 19: Retirement Planning

Goals

1. Ensure an adequate financial position at the time you retire.
2. Reduce the tax liability on your present income.

Analysis

1. At www.msn.com, click on the tab "Money." Scroll to the bottom of the page and click on "Site Map." Scroll down till you reach "Retirement" under "Planning Home." Click on "Retirement Planner" and then click on "Set Up Your Plan." Use the calculator to determine the amount of savings you will need to retire.
2. The next step is to determine how much money you must save per year, the return you must earn, and the savings period to meet your goal for retirement savings. Experiment with different inputs in the calculator in the Excel software.

Future Value of an Annuity

Payment per Period	
Number of Periods	
Interest Rate per Period	
Future Value	

Make any necessary adjustments to your personal cash flow statement.

Personal Cash Flow Statement

Cash Inflows	**This Month**
Disposable (after-tax) income	
Interest on deposits	
Dividend payments	
Other	
Total Cash Inflows	
Cash Outflows	
Rent	
Cable TV	
Electricity and water	
Telephone	
Groceries	
Health care insurance and expenses	
Clothing	
Car expenses (insurance, maintenance, and gas)	
Recreation	
Other	
Total Cash Outflows	
Net Cash Flows	

3. When examining retirement plans, keep in mind that tax benefits are important criteria. In the right-hand column of the following table, indicate how suitable the plan options are for you.

Type of Retirement Plan	Benefits	Suitability
Employer's Retirement Plan	Employee contributions are tax-deferred; employer may match contributions	
Traditional IRA or Roth IRA	Contribute up to $3,000 per year (tax-deferred) to a traditional IRA. Alternatively, contribute up to $3,000 annually to a Roth IRA after taxes; the withdrawal at retirement will not be taxed.	
Annuities	Contribute money to an annuity to supplement any other retirement plan. The only tax advantage is that any income earned on the investment is not taxed until withdrawal at retirement.	

4. Use the 401(k) planner template to see how your savings can grow. The Excel software will present a complete analysis based on your input in the table below.

401(k) Planner

401(k) Contribution per paycheck	
401(k) Employer match per paycheck	
Paychecks per year (12, 24, 26, and 52)	
Expected annual rate of return	
Age as of the end of this tax year	
Anticipated retirement age	
Current value of 401(k)	
Date (the "as of" date for the current value)	
Enter the date of the year end	
Marginal Tax Rate (State plus Federal)	

Tax Deferred 401(k) Plan Growth

Age	Estimated 401k Value

Taxable Savings Plan Growth

Age	Estimated Savings Value

Pre-tax retirement income*

From retirement age to 90 years old Monthly Income

Pre-tax retirement income*

From retirement age to 90 years old Monthly Income

* The Excel software templates will calculate this information and create a chart showing your investment growth.

Decisions

1. How much savings do you need to support you during retirement? [   ]

2. How much will you contribute to your retirement? What type of plan(s) will you contribute to?

[   ]

3. What are the present-day tax savings from your retirement planning? [   ]

Chapter 20: Estate Planning

Goals

1. Create a will.
2. Establish a plan for trusts or gifts if your estate is subject to high taxes.
3. Decide whether to create a living will or assign power of attorney.

Analysis

1. At the msn.com site, learn more about how equipped you are to create your own will by taking the "make-a-will quiz." Click on the "Money" tab. Scroll to the bottom of the page and click on "Site Map." Scroll down till you reach "Make-a-will quiz" under "Planning Home," "Retirement," "More tools."
2. Determine the size of your estate by reviewing your personal balance sheet and filling out the table below. (If you enter this information in the Excel template, the software will create a pie chart based on your input.)

Gross Estate	Amounts
Cash	
Stocks and bonds	
Notes and mortgages	
Annuities	
Retirement benefits	
Personal residence	
Other real estate	
Insurance	
Automobiles	
Artwork	
Jewelry	
Other (furniture, collectibles, etc.)	
Gross Estate	

3. Next, consider the following estate planning issues. Indicate your action plan in the right-hand column.

Issue	Status
Possible heirs and executor to my estate?	
Tax implications on my estate?	
Are trusts and gifts needed?	
Power of attorney necessary?	
Durable power of attorney necessary?	
Is a living will appropriate?	

Decisions

1. Will you create a will on your own or with an attorney's assistance? What special stipulations (for an heir or executor, or donations to charity) will you include?

2. Do you need to establish trusts or gifts to reduce your estate's tax liability?

3. Will you assign power of attorney and/or durable power of attorney?

Chapter 21: Integrating the Components of a Financial Plan

Goals

1. Review your completed financial plan.
2. Record the location of your important documents.

Analysis

1. Congratulations! You've now completed your financial plan. Remember that financial planning is an ongoing task. Use the following table as a reminder to review key parts of your financial plan.

Item	When Reviewed	Date Of Review
Short-term goals	As needed	
Intermediate-term goals	Annually	
Long-term goals	Annually	
Personal cash flow statement	Annually	
Personal balance sheet	Annually	
Tax situation	Annually, before year end	
Selection of financial institution	Biannually	
Credit report	Annually	
Loans	As needed	
Risk tolerance	Every 2-3 years	
Portfolio and asset allocation including stocks, bonds, and money market instruments	Annually	
Property and casualty insurance needs	Annually	
Insurance needs (life, health, auto)	As dictated by critical events	
Retirement plan	Annually	
Will and estate planning	As dictated by critical events	

2. Now that your plan is complete, store it for safekeeping. Along with your financial plan, keep a record of the location of your key assets and financial documents. Use the following template as a guide.

Location of Important Documents

Estate Related

Estate Related	Location
Wills / Trusts	
Letter of Last Instruction	
Other	
Other	

Insurance

Insurance	
Life	
Health	
Disability	
Auto	
Other	
Other	

Certificates and Deeds

Certificates and Deeds	
Automobile Titles	
Real Estate Deeds	
Birth Certificates	
Marriage Certificate	
Passports	
Other	
Other	

Investments And Savings

Investments And Savings	
Certificates of Deposit	
Stock Certificates	
Passbooks	
Mutual Fund Records	
Other	
Other	

Tax Records

Tax Records	
Last Year's Tax Return	
Last 7 Years of Tax Records	
Other	
Other	

Loans And Credit Cards

Loans And Credit Cards	
Loan Notes (still outstanding)	
List of Credit Card Numbers	
Other	
Other	

3. For those of you who have completed the software templates throughout the semester, you can now print out the final versions of your critical financial planning documents for safekeeping.

    •   Click on the tab "Your Financial Planning Documents" for the goals you've established in Chapter 1 and your final version of this document, as well as your personal cash flow statement and personal balance sheet from Chapter 2 and the final version of these documents. You will also find your asset allocation chart. Evaluate these documents to see how your financial plans have evolved throughout the course of the semester.

    •   Click on the tab "Your Financial Planning Decisions" for a summary of the decisions you have made in each chapter.

    Store printouts of the above documents in the folder at the back of this workbook, along with your home inventory, schedule for reviewing your financial plan, and location of important documents templates.

The Sampson Family: A Continuing Case

Chapter 1: Overview of a Financial Plan

Case Questions

1. Help the Sampsons summarize their current financial position, their goals, and their plans for achieving their goals by filing out the following templates.

CURRENT FINANCIAL POSITION

Major Assets	Amount
Savings (High, Medium, or Low)	
Money Owed	
Salary	

FINANCIAL GOALS

	Goal 1. Purchase new car for Sharon this year	Goal 2. Pay for children's college education 12-17 years from now	Goal 3. Set aside money for retirement
How to Achieve the Goal			
How to Implement the Plan			
How to Evaluate the Plan			

2. The Sampsons are considering consulting a financial advisor. Advise Dave and Sharon on the pros and cons of using the services of a financial advisor.

Chapter 2: Planning with Personal Financial Statements

Case Questions

1. Using the information in the text, prepare a personal cash flow statement for the Sampsons.

Personal Cash Flow Statement

Cash Inflows   **This Month**

_____   _____

_____   _____

_____   _____

_____   _____

Total Cash Inflows   _____

Cash Outflows

   Include categories for cash outflows as follows:

     Rent/Mortgage

     Cable Include TV   _____

     Electricity and water   _____

     Telephone   _____

     Groceries   _____

     Health care insurance and expenses   _____

     Clothing   _____

     Car expenses (insurance, maintenance, and gas)   _____

     Recreation   _____

     Other   _____

Total Cash Outflows   _____

Net Cash Flows   _____

2. Based on their personal cash flow statement, will the Sampsons be able to meet their savings goals? If not, how do you recommend that they revise their personal cash flow statement in order to achieve their savings goals?

3. Prepare a personal balance sheet for the Sampsons.

Personal Balance Sheet

Assets

Liquid Assets	
Cash	
Checking account	
Savings account	
Total liquid assets	
Household Assets	
Home	
Car	
Furniture	
Total household assets	
Investment Assets	
Stocks	
Bonds	
Mutual Funds	
Total investment assets	
Total Assets	

Liabilities and Net Worth

Current Liabilities	
Loans	
Credit card balance	
Total current liabilities	
Long-Term Liabilities	
Mortgage	
Car loan	
Total long-term liabilities	
Total Liabilities	

Net Worth	

4. What is the Sampsons' net worth? Based on the personal cash flow statement that you prepared in question 2, do you expect that their net worth will increase or decrease in the future? Why?

5. Dave's uncle has offered to provide a loan to pay for Sharon's new car. What are the advantages and disadvantages if the Sampsons accept his offer?

Chapter 3: Applying Time Value Concepts

Case Questions

1. Help the Sampsons determine how much they will have for the children's education by calculating how much $3,600 in annual savings will accumulate to if they earn interest of (a) 5 percent and (b) 7 percent. Next, determine how much $4,800 in annual savings will accumulate to if they earn interest of (a) 5 percent and (b) 7 percent.

Savings Accumulated Over the Next 12 Years
(Based on Plan to Save $3,600 per Year)

Amount Saved Per Year	$3,600	$3,600
Interest Rate	5%	7%
Years	12	12
Future Value of Savings		

Savings Accumulated Over the Next 12 Years
(Based on Plan to Save $4,800 per Year)

Amount Saved Per Year	$4,800	$4,800
Interest Rate	5%	7%
Years	12	12
Future Value of Savings		

2. What is the impact of the higher interest rate of 7 percent on the Sampsons' accumulated savings?

3. What is the impact of the higher savings of $4,800 on their accumulated savings?

4. If the Sampsons set a goal to save $70,000 for their children's college education in 12 years, how would you determine the yearly savings necessary to achieve this goal? How much would they have to save by the end of each year to achieve this goal, assuming a 5 percent annual interest rate?

Calculator: Savings Needed Each Year

Future Value	$70,000
Interest Rate	5%
Years	12
Savings Needed Each Year	

Chapter 4: Using Tax Concepts for Planning

Case Questions

1. Help the Sampsons estimate their federal income taxes for this year by filling in the following template.

Gross Income   _____

Retirement Plan Contribution   _____

Adjusted Gross Income   _____

Deductions

    Interest Expense   _____

    Real Estate Taxes   _____

    Contributions   _____   _____

      _____

Exemptions ($3,000 each)   _____

Taxable Income   _____

Tax Liability Before Tax Credits
(use 15% tax bracket)   _____

Child Tax Credit(s)   _____

Tax Liability   _____

2. The Sampsons think that it will be very difficult for them to pay the full amount of their taxes at this time. Consequently, they are thinking about underreporting their actual income on their tax return. What would you tell the Sampsons in response to this idea?"

Chapter 5: Banking and Interest Rates

Case Questions

1. Advise the Sampsons on the maturity to select when investing their savings in a CD for a down payment on a car. What are the advantages or disadvantages of the relatively short-term maturities versus the longer-term maturities?

2. Advise the Sampsons on the maturity to select when investing their savings for their children's education. Describe any advantages or disadvantages of the relatively short-term maturities versus the longer-term maturities.

3. If you thought that interest rates were going to rise in the next few months, how might this affect the advice that you give the Sampsons?

Chapter 6: Managing Your Money

Case Questions

1. Based on the cash flow statement and personal finance balance sheet, do the Sampsons have adequate liquidity to cover their recurring cash flows and planned monthly savings in the long run? If not, what level of savings should they maintain for liquidity purposes?

2. Advise the Sampsons on money market investments they should consider to provide them with adequate liquidity.

Chapter 7: Managing Your Credit

Case Questions

1. Compare the amount of interest that the Sampsons are earning on their savings and paying on their credit card debt by completing the following template.

Savings

Interest rate earned on savings	5%
Savings balance	
Annual interest earned on savings	

Paying Off Credit Balance

Interest rate paid on credit	18%
Credit balance	
Annual interest paid on credit	

2. Advise the Sampsons on whether they should continue making minimum payments on their credit card or use money from their savings to pay off the credit balance.

3. Explain how the Sampsons' credit card decisions are related to their budget.

Chapter 8: Personal Loans

Case Questions

1. Advise the Sampsons on possible loan maturities. Go to http://loan.yahoo.com/a/autocalc.html and click on "Loan Payment Calculator." Input information to determine the possible monthly car payments for a three-year (36-month) payment period, a four-year (48-month) payment period, and a five-year (60-month) period. Enter the results in the following table:

	Three-Year (36-month) Periods	Four-Year (48-month) Periods	Five-Year (60-month) Periods
Interest rate	7%	7%	7%
Monthly payment			
Total finance paments			
Total payments including the down payment and the trade-in			

2. What are the tradeoffs among the three alternative loan maturities?

3. Based on the information on finance payments that you retrieved from the loan payment Web site, advise the Sampsons on the best loan maturity for their needs.

4. At a recent family gathering, a relative offered to pay for the portion of the car's price that the Sampsons plan to finance. The Sampsons are considering the offer. Tell the Sampsons why such a loan may cause friction and offer a possible solution.

Chapter 9: Purchasing and Financing a Home

Case Questions

1. Use a Web site or a financial calculator to determine the monthly mortgage payment (excluding property taxes and insurance) on a $90,000 mortgage if the Sampsons obtain a new 30-year mortgage at the 8 percent interest rate. (One Web site that can be used for this purpose is http://loan.yahoo.com/m/mortcalc.html.)

Mortgage loan	$90,000
Interest rate	8%
Years	30
Loan payment	

2. The Sampsons expect that they will not move for at least three years. Advise the Sampsons on whether they should refinance their mortgage by comparing the savings of refinancing with the costs.

Current mortgage payment	
New mortgage payment	
Monthly savings	
Annual savings	
Marginal tax rate	
Increase in taxes	
Annual savings after-tax	
Years in house after refinancing	
Total savings	

3. Why might your advice about refinancing change in the future?

Chapter 10: Auto and Homeowner's Insurance

Case Questions

1. Advise the Sampsons regarding their car insurance. Do they have enough insurance? Do they have too much insurance? How might they be able to reduce their premium?

2. Sharon has recently been in an accident that was caused by a drunk driver. The other driver did not receive a ticket for driving while intoxicated. Sharon is considering suing the other driver for emotional distress. Do you think the lawsuit will be successful?

3. Consider the Sampsons homeowner's insurance. Do they have enough insurance? Do they have too much insurance? Is increasing their deductible well advised?

Chapter 11: Health and Disability Insurance

Case Questions

1. Make suggestions to the Sampsons regarding their health insurance. Do you think they should switch from the HMO to a PPO? Why or why not?

2. Do you think the Sampsons should purchase disability insurance? Why or why not?

3. Should Dave and Sharon purchase long-term care insurance? Why or why not?

Chapter 12: Life Insurance

Case Questions

1. Determine the present value of the insurance benefits that could provide $40,000 over the next 15 years for the Sampson family. Assume that the insurance payment could be invested to earn 6 percent interest over time.

Annual amount	$40,000
Number of years	15
Annual interest rate	6%
Present value	

2. Considering the insurance benefits needed to provide $40,000 over the next 15 years, plus the additional $330,000 of insurance coverage, what amount of insurance coverage is needed?

3. Given the total amount of insurance coverage needed and Dave's present age (30 years old), estimate the premium that the Sampsons would pay using one of the insurance Web sites mentioned in the chapter (such as http://insweb.com).

4. Dave Sampson is a social smoker. Since he only smokes occasionally, he would like to omit this information from his life insurance application. Advise Dave on this course of action.

Chapter 13: Investing Fundamentals

Case Questions

1. Compare the returns from investing in bank CDs to the possible returns from stock over the next 12 years by filling in the following template:

Savings Accumulated Over the Next 12 Years

	CD: Annual Return = 5%	Weak Stock Market Conditions	Strong Stock Market Conditions
Amount invested per year	$3600	$3600	$3600
Annual return	5%	2%	9%
FVIFA (n = 12 years)			
Value of investments in 12 years			

2. Explain to the Sampsons why there is a tradeoff when investing in bank CDs versus stock to support their children's future college education.

3. Advise the Sampsons on whether they should invest their money each month in bank CDs in stocks, or in some combination of the two, to save for their children's college education.

4. The Sampsons are considering investing in an IPO of a high-tech firm, since they have heard that the return on IPOs can be very high. Advise the Sampsons on this course of action.

Chapter 14: Stock Analysis and Valuation

Case Questions

1. Advise the Sampsons as to whether they should put all of their investments in technology stocks.

2. Should the information the Sampsons read on the Web site affect how they invest in stocks?

3. Dave Sampson recently received an annual report from a corporation and is very impressed by the optimism expressed in the report about the firm's future. Dave researched the firm and found that the firm has a very low PE ratio relative to other firms in the industry. He therefore believes the stock to be undervalued and would like to invest in it. What do you think about Dave's plan?

Chapter 15: Investing in Stocks

Case Questions

1. Offer advice to the Sampsons on whether they should buy these stocks based on the information on the Web site.

2. Other Web sites identify firms that were top performers the previous day. Should the Sampsons buy these stocks? Explain.

Chapter 16: Investing in Bonds

Case Questions

1. Should the Sampsons consider investing a portion of their savings in bonds to save for their children's education? Why or why not?

2. If the Sampsons should purchase bonds, what maturities should they consider, keeping in mind their investment goal?

3. If the Sampsons should consider bonds, should they invest in corporate bonds or municipal bonds? Factor the return they would receive after tax liabilities into your analysis, based on the bonds having a $1,000 par value and the Sampsons being in a 27 percent marginal tax bracket.

After-Tax Rate Computation

Corporate bond yield	
Marginal tax rate	
After-Tax Rate	
Annual after-tax interest ($)	

4. The Sampsons have read that many corporate bonds have recently been downgraded due to questionable financial statements. However, the Sampsons are not concerned with this, since the corporate bond they are considering is highly rated. Explain the possible impact of a downgrade of the corporate bond to the Sampsons, given their financial goals.

Chapter 17: Investing in Mutual Funds

Case Questions

1. Why might mutual funds be more appropriate investments for the Sampsons than individual stocks or bonds?

2. Should the Sampsons invest their savings in mutual funds? Why or why not?

3. What types of mutual funds should the Sampsons consider, given their investment objective?

Chapter 18: Asset Allocation

Case Questions

1. Advise the Sampsons regarding the soundness of their tentative decision to invest all of their children's college education money in a biotechnology mutual fund.

2. The Sampsons are aware that diversification is important. Therefore, they have decided that they will initially invest in one biotechnology mutual fund and then invest in three other biotechnology mutual funds as they accumulate more money. In this way, even if one mutual fund performs poorly, they expect that the other biotechnology mutual funds will perform well. How can the Sampsons diversify their investments more effectively?

3. A good friend of Dave's just called him up and informed him that the company he works for will announce a new product tomorrow that will revolutionize the industry the friend works in. Dave is very excited about the prospective jump in the stock price. He is ready to buy some stock in the friend's company. Advise Dave on this course of action.

Chapter 19: Retirement Planning

Case Questions

1. If Dave and his employer contribute a total of $10,000 annually, how much will that amount accumulate to over the next 30 years, at which time Dave and his wife Sharon hope to retire?

Future Value of an Annuity

Contribution	$10,000
Years	30
Annual rate of return	
Future Value	

2. Assuming that Dave's marginal tax bracket is 27 percent, by how much should his federal taxes decline this year if he contributes $7,000 to his retirement account?

3. Assuming that Dave contributes $7,000 to his retirement account and that his taxes are lower as a result, by how much are Dave's cash flows reduced over the coming year? (Refer to your answer in question 2 when solving this problem.)

4. If Dave contributes $7,000 to his retirement account, he will have less cash inflows as a result. How can the Sampsons afford to make this contribution? Suggest some ways that they may be able to offset the reduction in cash inflows by reexamining the cash flow statement you created for them in Chapter 2.

5. Dave's employer has strongly urged him to invest his entire 401(k) contribution in the company's stock. Advise Dave on how to handle this situation.

Chapter 20: Estate Planning

Case Questions

1. Advise the Sampsons on how they can plan their estate to achieve their financial goals.

2. What important consideration are the Sampsons overlooking in their estate planning goals?

3. Dave recently met with an estate planner who offered to create an elaborate estate plan without asking Dave specific questions. What should Dave have done prior to meeting with the estate planner?

Chapter 21: Integrating the Components of a Financial Plan

Case Questions

1. Explain how the Sampsons' budgeting affects all of their other financial planning decisions.

2. How are the Sampsons' liquidity and investment decisions related?

3. In what ways are the Sampsons' financing and investing decisions related? What should they do in the future before asking advice from investment advisers?

4. Explain how the Sampsons' retirement planning decisions are related to their investing decisions.

5. How likely is it that the Sampsons will achieve their financial goals, now that they have captured them in a financial plan? What activity must they periodically undertake?

Brad Brooks: A Continuing Case

Part 1: Tools for Financial Planning

Case Questions

1. a. Prepare personal financial statements for Brad, including a personal cash flow statement and personal balance sheet.

Personal Cash Flow Statement

Cash Inflows	This Month
_____	_____
_____	_____
_____	_____
_____	_____
Total Cash Inflows	_____
Cash Outflows	
_____	_____
_____	_____
_____	_____
_____	_____
_____	_____
_____	_____
_____	_____
_____	_____
_____	_____
_____	_____
Total Cash Outflows	_____
Net Cash Flows	_____

Personal Balance Sheet

Assets

Liquid Assets	
Cash	
Checking account	
Savings account	
Other liquid assets	
Total liquid assets	
Household Assets	
Home	
Car	
Furniture	
Other household assets	
Total household assets	
Investment Assets	
Stocks	
Bonds	
Mutual Funds	
Other investments	
Total investment assets	
Total Assets	

Liabilities and Net Worth

Current Liabilities	
Loans	
Credit card balance	
Other current liabilities	
Total current liabilities	
Long-Term Liabilities	
Mortgage	
Car loan	
Other long-term liabilities	
Total long-term liabilities	
Total Liabilities	

Net Worth

b. Based on these statements, make specific recommendations to Brad as to what he needs to do to achieve his goals of paying off his credit card balance and saving for retirement.

c. What additional goals could you recommend to Brad for both the short and long term?

2. Consider Brad's goal to retire in 20 years by saving $4,000 per year starting five years from now.

a. Based on your analysis of Brad's cash flow and your recommendations, is saving $4,000 per year a realistic goal? If not, what other goal would you advise?

b. In order for Brad to know what his $4,000 per year will accumulate to in 20 years, what additional assumption (or piece of information) must he make (or have)?

c. Assuming that Brad invests the $4,000 per year for 20 years starting five years from now in something that will return 12 percent, how much will he?

Future Value of an Annuity

Payment per Period	$4,000
Number of Periods	20
Interest Rate per Period	12%
Future Value	

d. Compare the alternative of investing $4000 every year for 25 years beginning today with Brad's plan to invest $4000 every year for 20 years beginning five years from now. How much additional funds will Brad have to save each year to end up with the same amount that he would have in 25 years if he started saving now instead of five years from now? (Again, assume a 12 percent annual return.)

Future Value of an Annuity

Payment per Period	$4,000
Number of Periods	15
Interest Rate per Period	12%
Future Value	

3. Develop three or four suggestions that could help Brad reduce his income tax exposure.

Suggestions to Reduce Taxes	Pros	Cons

4. Would any of your recommendations in questions 1 through 3 change if Brad were 45? If he were 60? Why or why not?

5. After you informed Brad of his negative monthly net cash flow, Brad indicated that he may delay paying his credit card bills for a couple of months to reduce his cash outflows. What is your response to your friend's idea?

Part 2: Managing Your Liquidity

Case Questions

1. Assuming that you could convince Brad to maintain checking, savings, and retirement accounts, discuss the pros and cons of various types of financial institutions where Brad could maintain his:

    a. checking account;
    b. savings account;
    c. retirement accounts.

    Be sure to comment on Brad's idea to find financial institutions that can give him advice on his financial decisions.

2. If Brad's stocks double in value over the next five years, what annual return would he realize? (Hint: Use the future value table.) Based on his projected annualized return would it be advisable to sell the stocks to pay off his credit card? Should Brad consider shopping for a new credit card?

3. How would you address Brad's reluctance to pay off his credit card balance? Show him what he could earn in five years if he paid it off and invested the interest saved at 6 percent.

Future Value of a Lump Sum

Yearly Savings	
Number of Periods	
Interest Rate per Period	
Future Value	

4. Would your advice change if Brad were:

   a. 45 years old?;
   b. 60 years old?

5. Prepare a written or oral report on your findings and recommendations for Brad.

Part 3: Personal Financing

Case Questions

1. Refer to Brad's personal cash flow statement that you developed in Part 1. Recompute his expenses to determine if Brad can afford to:

   a. Purchase the new car;
   b. Lease a new car;
   c. Purchase his condo;
   d. Purchase both the car and condo;
   e. Lease the car and purchase the condo.

Personal Cash Flow Statement

Cash Inflows	This Month
Total Cash Inflows	
Cash Outflows	
Total Cash Outflows	
Net Cash Flows	

2. Brad's rich uncle has offered to provide Brad with a loan for the closing costs and the down payment needed to purchase the condo. Brad exclaims, "This is great. I don't even need a loan contract!" Advise Brad on the situation.

3. What are the advantages and disadvantages to Brad of leasing rather than purchasing a car?

4. Based on the information you provided, Brad decides not to buy the condo at this time. How can he save the necessary funds to purchase a condo or house in the future? Be specific in your recommendations.

Future Value of an Annuity

Payment per Period	
Number of Periods	
Interest Rate per Period	
Future Value	

5. How would your advice to Brad differ if he were:
   a. 45 years old?;
   b. 60 years old?

6. Prepare a written or oral report on your findings and recommendations to Brad.

Part 4: Protecting Your Wealth

Case Questions

1. Concerning Brad's life insurance decision, comment on:
   a. His need for life insurance;
   b. If you see any reasons for life insurance in (a), is whole life the best way to meet it?;
   c. His plan to use the whole life policy's loan feature as a means for maintaining liquidity.

2. Regarding Brad's auto insurance decision, comment on:
   a. His plan to add different types of coverage to his auto insurance policy;
   b. The associated costs of adding different types of coverage to his auto insurance policy;
   c. Any resulting negative consequences of switching to a more inexpensive auto insurance company;
   d. Any other factors Brad should consider before switching insurance companies.

3. Describe renter's insurance to Brad. What determines whether renter's insurance is appropriate for Brad?

4. Describe to Brad how he could benefit from a PPO. Are there any negative factors Brad needs to know about if he seriously considers switching to a PPO? Consider Brad's cash flow situation from the previous parts when answering this question.

Part 5: Personal Investing

Case Questions

1. Comment on each of the following elements of Brad's plan:
   a. Level of diversification with three technology stocks;
   b. View on bonds and not including them in his portfolio;
   c. Trading online;
   d. Margin trading;
   e. Source of information ("hot tips").

2. Given Brad's lack of knowledge of investing and limited time to learn or do research, what might be the best option for Brad to pursue and still get the benefit of the potential growth in the technology sector?

3. What factors will influence Brad's asset allocation? Based on these factors, what might be a suitable sample portfolio for Brad?

4. How would your answer to the sample portfolio part of question three be affected if Brad were:
   a. 45 years old?;
   b. 60 years old?

5. Explain to Brad why misleading financial statements may be more common than be believes and why misleading financial statements can negatively affect a stock's price.

6.   Prepare a written or oral report on your findings and recommendations to Brad.

Part 6: Retirement and Estate Planning

Case Questions

1. With regard to Brad's revised retirement plans:

    a. How much will he have in 30 years if he invests $300 per month at 8%? Do not consider the employer's matched contribution at this point.

Future Value of an Annuity

Payment per year	
Number of years	30
Annual interest rate	8%
Future Value	

    b. How much will he have to save per month at 8% to reach his $500,000 goal in 20 years? In 30 years?

Amount to be Accumulated	$500,000
Number of Years	20
Annual Interest Rate	8%
Annual Deposit	
Monthly Deposit	

Amount to be Accumulated	$500,000
Number of Years	30
Annual Interest Rate	8%
Annual Deposit	
Monthly Deposit	

    c. What impact could retiring 10 year's earlier have on Brad's current standard of living?

    d. If Brad takes advantage of his employer's match, what will be the impact on his retirement savings (assume an 8 percent return).

Future Value of an Annuity

Payment per year	
Number of years	20
Annual interest rate	8%
Future Value	

Future Value of an Annuity

Payment per year	
Number of years	30
Annual interest rate	8%
Future Value	

e. What other options are available to Brad to save for his retirement? Give the pros and cons of each.

2. If Brad really wishes to provide for his nephews' college education, how can a will help him achieve that goal? What else might Brad consider to assure his nephews' college education?

3. Would your advice in questions 1–2 change if Brad were:
   a. 45 years old?;
   b. 60 years old?

4. Prepare a written or oral report on your findings and recommendations to Brad.

Financial Planning Online Resources

In recognition of the Internet's ability to facilitate every aspect of financial planning, *Personal Finance* includes Financial Planning Online features throughout every chapter. Each Financial Planning Online includes a full-color screenshot of the specified Web site along with the Internet address and a detailed description of what the site provides. Use the below list of the Financial Planning Online features as a reference when completing the exercises in this Financial Planning Workbook and utilizing the accompanying Financial Planning Software.

Here is a complete listing of the Financial Planning Online features:

1.1 Financial Planning Online: Financial Planning Tools for You
http://finance.yahoo.com/

2.1 Financial Planning Online: Budgeting Tips
http://www.dallasfed.org/htm/wealth/index.html

2.2 Financial Planning Online: The Impact of Reduced Spending
http://www.financenter.com/products/sellingtools/calculators/budget

2.3 Financial Planning Online: Budgeting Advice
http://www.financenter.com/products/sellingtools/calculators/budget

3.1 Financial Planning Online: Paying Your Bills Online
http://moneycentral.msn.com

3.2 Financial Planning Online: Estimating the Future Value of Your Savings
http://moneycentral.msn.com/investor/calcs/n_savapp/main.asp

4.1 Financial Planning Online: Internal Revenue Service
http://www.irs.gov

4.2 Financial Planning Online: State Income Tax Rates
http://taxes.yahoo.com/statereport.html

4.3 Financial Planning Online: Tax Information Resource
http://www.taxplanet.com

4.4 Financial Planning Online: Estimating Your Taxes
http://taxes.yahoo.com/estimator

5.1 Financial Planning Online: Internet Banking
http://www.chicagofed.org

5.2 Financial Planning Online: Financial Institutions That Can Serve Your Needs
http://dir.yahoo.com/business_and_economy/finance_and_investment/banking/

5.3 Financial Planning Online: Current Interest Rate Quotations
http://www.bloomberg.com/markets/rates.html

5.4 Financial Planning Online: Updated Treasury Yields
http://www.bloomberg.com

5.5 Financial Planning Online: Fed's Upcoming Meetings
http://www.bloomberg.com/bbn/fedwatch.html

6.1 Financial Planning Online: Deposit Rates Offered by Banks
http://www.bankrate.com/brm/rate/dep_home.asp

6.2 Financial Planning Online: Impact of Different Deposit Rates on Your Wealth
http://www.financenter.com/products/sellingtools/calculators

9.7 Financial Planning Online: Should You Obtain a 15-Year or a 30-Year Mortgage?
http://www.financenter.com/products/sellingtools/calculators

9.8 Financial Planning Online: Should You Obtain a Fixed- or an Adjustable-Rate Mortgage?
http://www.financenter.com/products/sellingtools/calculators/

9.9 Financial Planning Online: Should You Rent or Buy?
http://loan.yahoo.com/m/

10.1 Financial Planning Online: Reviews of Insurance Companies
http://www.gomez.com

10.2 Financial Planning Online: How Much Car Insurance Coverage Do You Need?
http://insurance.yahoo.com/auto.html

10.3 Financial Planning Online: Purchasing Homeowner's Insurance
http://moneycentral.msn.com/articles/insure/home/contents.asp

10.4 Financial Planning Online: Renter's Insurance Quotation
http://insurance.yahoo.com/r1.html

11.1 Financial Planning Online: Should You Enroll in an HMO or a PPO?
http://insurance.yahoo.com/lh/health.html

11.2 Financial Planning Online: Medicare Coverage
http://www.medicare.gov/Basics/overview.asp

12.1 Financial Planning Online: Buying Term Life Insurance
http://moneycentral.msn.com/

12.2 Financial Planning Online: Should You Buy Whole Life or Term Insurance?
http://www.financenter.com/products/sellingtools/calculators

12.3 Financial Planning Online: Return on Your Whole Life Insurance Policy
http://www.financenter.com/products/sellingtools/calculators

12.4 Financial Planning Online: How Much Life Insurance Do You Need?
http://moneycentral.msn.com/investor/calcs/n_life/main.asp

13.1 Financial Planning Online: IPOs
http://www.ipo.com

13.2 Financial Planning Online: Price Trends of Your Stocks
http://finance.yahoo.com/

14.1 Financial Planning Online:
http://www.bloomberg.com

14.2 Financial Planning Online: Determining Industry Norms
http://biz.yahoo.com/research/indgrp

14.3 Financial Planning Online: Stock Market Quotations and Conditions
http://www.bloomberg.com/bbn/economies.html

14.4 Financial Planning Online: Earnings Estimates for Valuing Your Stock
http://biz.yahoo.com/research/earncal/today.html

14.5 Financial Planning Online: Screening Stocks for Investment Decisions
http://screen.yahoo.com/stocks.html

15.1 Financial Planning Online: Analyst Recommendations
http://finance.yahoo.com/?u

15.2 Financial Planning Online: Trading Stocks Online
http://www.etrade.com

15.3 Financial Planning Online: Stock Market Summary
http://www.bloomberg.com

15.4 Financial Planning Online: Stock Index Quotations
http://finance.yahoo.com/m1?u

16.1 Financial Planning Online: Your Bond's Yield
http://www.financenter.com/products/sellingtools/calculators

16.2 Financial Planning Online: Municipal Bond Quotations
http://www.bloomberg.com/markets/psamuni.html

16.3 Financial Planning Online: Today's Events That Could Affect Bond Prices
http://www.businessweek.com/investor/

17.1 Financial Planning Online: Index Mutual Funds
http://www.indexfunds.com/

17.2 Financial Planning Online: Return from Investing in Mutual Funds
http://www.bloomberg.com

17.3 Financial Planning Online: Mutual Fund Reports
http://moneycentral.msn.com

17.4 Financial Planning Online: Online Services by Mutual Funds
http://www.vanguard.com

17.5 Financial Planning Online: Diversifying among Mutual Funds
http://www.mfea.com

18.1 Financial Planning Online: Correlations among Stock Returns
http://finance.yahoo.com/?u

18.2 Financial Planning Online: Advice on Your Asset Allocation
http://moneycentral.msn.com/investor/calcs/assetall/main.asp

19.1 Financial Planning Online: Request a Social Security Statement
http://www.ssa.gov/top10.html

19.2 Financial Planning Online: Retirement Expense Calculator
http://moneycentral.msn.com/investor/calcs/n_retireq/main.asp

19.3 Financial Planning Online: Traditional IRA or Roth IRA?
http://www.financenter.com/products/sellingtools/calculators/ira/

19.4 Financial Planning Online: How to Build Your Retirement Plan
http://www.quicken.com/retirement/planner

20.1 Financial Planning Online: Quiz for Preparing Your Own Will
http://moneycentral.msn.com/articles/retire/will/tlwillq.asp

20.2 Financial Planning Online: How to Build Your Estate Plan
http://moneycentral.msn.com/retire/home.asp

20.3 Financial Planning Online: Legal Advice on Estate Planning
http://www.nolo.com

21.1 Financial Planning Online: Insight about Financial Planning Concepts
http://www.kiplinger.com

21.2 Financial Planning Online: A Synthesized Financial Plan
http://quicken.com/banking_and_credit/savings_calc

Notes

Notes

Notes

Notes